Assignment:

Instructor:

Course:

Due Date:

D1529784

Specifications

Will you be using a style guide, such as MLA, APA? If so, which. Also note any exceptions or special requirements you have for this essay.

What particular font, margin, and spacing requirements do you need?

Do you need a minimum number of sources?

Do you need peer reviewed sources?

Do you need primary sources, secondary sources, or both?

Do you need to reference one or more course texts? If so which texts, and and what chapters, pages, parts, or aspects should you reference?

Is there a minimum length the final draft should attain? If so, what is it?

Specifications

Are there additional materials required outside of those marked already in these specifications?

Will you be submitting the final draft by email, hardcopy, upload, or something else? Describe exactly how you will submit your final work.

How many drafts are due, and when are they due? List all of the drafts below, and their respective due dates.

Reader Expectations

MY READER CAN BE DESCRIBED AS...

Readers can generally be categorized as professionals, well informed general public, or ill-informed general public. Consider which of these broad categories your ideal reader falls into. Does the reader expect to be entertained, provided with new knowledge, or helped to solve a practical problem? **Choose only one.**

EXPERT
- ☐ Provided with knowledge
- ☐ Helped to solve a practical problem
- ☐ Entertained

GENERAL PUBLIC
- ☐ Provided with knowledge
- ☐ Helped to solve a practical problem
- ☐ Entertained

POLICY MAKER
- ☐ Provided with knowledge
- ☐ Helped to solve a practical problem
- ☐ Entertained

OTHER
- ☐ Provided with knowledge
- ☐ Helped to solve a practical problem
- ☐ Entertained

WHAT'S MY READER'S PERSPECTIVE?

Essays must generally make some kind of proposal. Does your proposal solve a problem that your ideal reader would recognize? Or might the proposal itself represent a new problem to them? If your ideal reader is unlikely to understand with or agree with your proposal, they may need to be convinced.

- ☐ The problem is already recognized by reader.
- ☐ The problem would be new to the reader.
- ☐ The reader sees no problem at all.

HOW WILL MY READER REACT?

Does your proposal contradict what the reader believes, and if so, how? Can you anticipate their response? Will showing the reader the steps that led you to your proposition convince them?

Reader Expectations

A P A

APA: make sure to list the sources alphabetically by their first entry.

APA

Doe, J.A., & Doe, J.B. (Year). Title of source. Title of Publication, volume number (if available), pages referenced, http://dx.doi.org/xx.xxx/yyyyy.

M L A

MLA: 8th Edition MLA works cited entries use a "container" metaphor; an article is contained within a newspaper; a chapter is contained within a book; an episode is contained within a series. There can be containers within containers (for example an article within a journal within a database). Location always refers to the location of the source within its container (for example, pp. 50-55). Use Version and Number only for periodicals (like academic journals and magazines); the edition is always part of the title. Make sure to list the sources by their first entry alphabetically.

MLA

Doe, Jane A., and John B. Doe. "Title of Source." Container. Contributers, Version, Number, Publisher, Publication Date, Location. Second Container. Publisher, Publication Date, Location.

Source Analysis

Source Checklist

- ☐ Authored by a scholar:
    - ☐ Authored by an expert:
    - ☐ Authored by an organization:
    - ☐ Unknown author
- ☐ Published
    - ☐ by a university press:
    - ☐ by another press:
    - ☐ Sponsored by an organization:
- ☐ Primary Source
    - ☐ Secondary Source
    - ☐ Tertiary Source
- ☐ Current
    - ☐ Historical Document
- ☐ Peer-reviewed by:
    - ☐ Critically reviewed by:
    - ☐ Cited by:
- ☐ Contains a bibliography
- ☐ Contains keywords
- ☐ Contains good quotes
- ☐ Connects to my argument
- ☐ Contradicts my argument

Who is the author? What are the author's credentials? What else has the author written? What is their stance on, or interest in, the topic?

Who is the publisher? What is the publisher's editorial policy? Is the publisher an imprint owned by another company, a website run by a government agency, or a private blog? What is the purpose, or mission, of the publisher?

Is the research current, and if not, what is the historical context in which it was produced? What is the general history of this document? Who are the original contributer(s) and author(s)? What other forces have shaped it, political, economic, or otherwise?

How does it support your argument? Explain how it supports your argument.

How does it contradict your argument? Paraphrase or use direct quote and explain the contradiction.

Promising entries from the source's bibliography:

Briefly summarize the source here.

Source Checklist

- ☐ Authored by a scholar:
    - ☐ Authored by an expert:
    - ☐ Authored by an organization:
    - ☐ Unknown author
- ☐ Published
    - ☐ by a university press:
    - ☐ by another press:
    - ☐ Sponsored by an organization:
- ☐ Primary Source
    - ☐ Secondary Source
    - ☐ Tertiary Source
- ☐ Current
    - ☐ Historical Document
- ☐ Peer-reviewed by:
    - ☐ Critically reviewed by:
    - ☐ Cited by:
- ☐ Contains a bibliography
- ☐ Contains keywords
- ☐ Contains good quotes
- ☐ Connects to my argument
- ☐ Contradicts my argument

Is the research current, and if not, what is the historical context in which it was produced? What is the general history of this document? Who are the original contributer(s) and author(s)? What other forces have shaped it, political, economic, or otherwise?

How does it support your argument? Explain how it supports your argument.

How does it contradict your argument? Paraphrase or use direct quote and explain the contradiction.

Promising entries from the source's bibliography:

Who is the author? What are the author's credentials? What else has the author written? What is their stance on, or interest in, the topic?

Briefly summarize the source here.

Who is the publisher? What is the publisher's editorial policy? Is the publisher an imprint owned by another company, a website run by a government agency, or a private blog? What is the purpose, or mission, of the publisher?

Source Checklist

- ☐ Authored by a scholar:
    - ☐ Authored by an expert:
    - ☐ Authored by an organization:
    - ☐ Unknown author
- ☐ Published
    - ☐ by a university press:
    - ☐ by another press:
    - ☐ Sponsored by an organization:
- ☐ Primary Source
    - ☐ Secondary Source
    - ☐ Tertiary Source
- ☐ Current
    - ☐ Historical Document
- ☐ Peer-reviewed by:
    - ☐ Critically reviewed by:
    - ☐ Cited by:
- ☐ Contains a bibliography
- ☐ Contains keywords
- ☐ Contains good quotes
- ☐ Connects to my argument
- ☐ Contradicts my argument

Is the research current, and if not, what is the historical context in which it was produced? What is the general history of this document? Who are the original contributer(s) and author(s)? What other forces have shaped it, political, economic, or otherwise?

How does it support your argument? Explain how it supports your argument.

How does it contradict your argument? Paraphrase or use direct quote and explain the contradiction.

Promising entries from the source's bibliography:

Who is the author? What are the author's credentials? What else has the author written? What is their stance on, or interest in, the topic?

Briefly summarize the source here.

Who is the publisher? What is the publisher's editorial policy? Is the publisher an imprint owned by another company, a website run by a government agency, or a private blog? What is the purpose, or mission, of the publisher?

SOURCE CHECKLIST

- ☐ Authored by a scholar:
  - ☐ Authored by an expert:
  - ☐ Authored by an organization:
  - ☐ Unknown author
- ☐ Published
  - ☐ by a university press:
  - ☐ by another press:
  - ☐ Sponsored by an organization:
- ☐ Primary Source
  - ☐ Secondary Source
  - ☐ Tertiary Source
- ☐ Current
  - ☐ Historical Document
- ☐ Peer-reviewed by:
  - ☐ Critically reviewed by:
  - ☐ Cited by:
- ☐ Contains a bibliography
- ☐ Contains keywords
- ☐ Contains good quotes
- ☐ Connects to my argument
- ☐ Contradicts my argument

Is the research current, and if not, what is the historical context in which it was produced? What is the general history of this document? Who are the original contributer(s) and author(s)? What other forces have shaped it, political, economic, or otherwise?

How does it support your argument? Explain how it supports your argument.

How does it contradict your argument? Paraphrase or use direct quote and explain the contradiction.

Promising entries from the source's bibliography:

Who is the author? What are the author's credentials? What else has the author written? What is their stance on, or interest in, the topic?

Briefly summarize the source here.

Who is the publisher? What is the publisher's editorial policy? Is the publisher an imprint owned by another company, a website run by a government agency, or a private blog? What is the purpose, or mission, of the publisher?

Source Checklist

- ☐ Authored by a scholar:
  - ☐ Authored by an expert:
  - ☐ Authored by an organization:
  - ☐ Unknown author
- ☐ Published
  - ☐ by a university press:
  - ☐ by another press:
  - ☐ Sponsored by an organization:
- ☐ Primary Source
  - ☐ Secondary Source
  - ☐ Tertiary Source
- ☐ Current
  - ☐ Historical Document
- ☐ Peer-reviewed by:
  - ☐ Critically reviewed by:
  - ☐ Cited by:
- ☐ Contains a bibliography
- ☐ Contains keywords
- ☐ Contains good quotes
- ☐ Connects to my argument
- ☐ Contradicts my argument

Is the research current, and if not, what is the historical context in which it was produced? What is the general history of this document? Who are the original contributer(s) and author(s)? What other forces have shaped it, political, economic, or otherwise?

How does it support your argument? Explain how it supports your argument.

How does it contradict your argument? Paraphrase or use direct quote and explain the contradiction.

Promising entries from the source's bibliography:

Who is the author? What are the author's credentials? What else has the author written? What is their stance on, or interest in, the topic?

Briefly summarize the source here.

Who is the publisher? What is the publisher's editorial policy? Is the publisher an imprint owned by another company, a website run by a government agency, or a private blog? What is the purpose, or mission, of the publisher?

Source Checklist

- ☐ Authored by a scholar:
  - ☐ Authored by an expert:
  - ☐ Authored by an organization:
  - ☐ Unknown author
- ☐ Published
  - ☐ by a university press:
  - ☐ by another press:
  - ☐ Sponsored by an organization:
- ☐ Primary Source
  - ☐ Secondary Source
  - ☐ Tertiary Source
- ☐ Current
  - ☐ Historical Document
- ☐ Peer-reviewed by:
  - ☐ Critically reviewed by:
  - ☐ Cited by:
- ☐ Contains a bibliography
- ☐ Contains keywords
- ☐ Contains good quotes
- ☐ Connects to my argument
- ☐ Contradicts my argument

Is the research current, and if not, what is the historical context in which it was produced? What is the general history of this document? Who are the original contributer(s) and author(s)? What other forces have shaped it, political, economic, or otherwise?

How does it support your argument? Explain how it supports your argument.

How does it contradict your argument? Paraphrase or use direct quote and explain the contradiction.

Promising entries from the source's bibliography:

Who is the author? What are the author's credentials? What else has the author written? What is their stance on, or interest in, the topic?

Briefly summarize the source here.

Who is the publisher? What is the publisher's editorial policy? Is the publisher an imprint owned by another company, a website run by a government agency, or a private blog? What is the purpose, or mission, of the publisher?

SOURCE CHECKLIST

- ☐ Authored by a scholar:
  - ☐ Authored by an expert:
  - ☐ Authored by an organization:
  - ☐ Unknown author
- ☐ Published
  - ☐ by a university press:
  - ☐ by another press:
  - ☐ Sponsored by an organization:
- ☐ Primary Source
  - ☐ Secondary Source
  - ☐ Tertiary Source
- ☐ Current
  - ☐ Historical Document
- ☐ Peer-reviewed by:
  - ☐ Critically reviewed by:
  - ☐ Cited by:
- ☐ Contains a bibliography
- ☐ Contains keywords
- ☐ Contains good quotes
- ☐ Connects to my argument
- ☐ Contradicts my argument

Is the research current, and if not, what is the historical context in which it was produced? What is the general history of this document? Who are the original contributer(s) and author(s)? What other forces have shaped it, political, economic, or otherwise?

How does it support your argument? Explain how it supports your argument.

How does it contradict your argument? Paraphrase or use direct quote and explain the contradiction.

Promising entries from the source's bibliography:

Who is the author? What are the author's credentials? What else has the author written? What is their stance on, or interest in, the topic?

Briefly summarize the source here.

Who is the publisher? What is the publisher's editorial policy? Is the publisher an imprint owned by another company, a website run by a government agency, or a private blog? What is the purpose, or mission, of the publisher?

Source Checklist

- ☐ Authored by a scholar:
  - ☐ Authored by an expert:
  - ☐ Authored by an organization:
  - ☐ Unknown author
- ☐ Published
  - ☐ by a university press:
  - ☐ by another press:
  - ☐ Sponsored by an organization:
- ☐ Primary Source
  - ☐ Secondary Source
  - ☐ Tertiary Source
- ☐ Current
  - ☐ Historical Document
- ☐ Peer-reviewed by:
  - ☐ Critically reviewed by:
  - ☐ Cited by:
- ☐ Contains a bibliography
- ☐ Contains keywords
- ☐ Contains good quotes
- ☐ Connects to my argument
- ☐ Contradicts my argument

Is the research current, and if not, what is the historical context in which it was produced? What is the general history of this document? Who are the original contributer(s) and author(s)? What other forces have shaped it, political, economic, or otherwise?

How does it support your argument? Explain how it supports your argument.

How does it contradict your argument? Paraphrase or use direct quote and explain the contradiction.

Promising entries from the source's bibliography:

Who is the author? What are the author's credentials? What else has the author written? What is their stance on, or interest in, the topic?

Briefly summarize the source here.

Who is the publisher? What is the publisher's editorial policy? Is the publisher an imprint owned by another company, a website run by a government agency, or a private blog? What is the purpose, or mission, of the publisher?

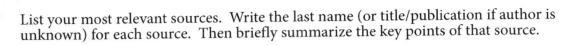

Intro Sketch

List your most relevant sources. Write the last name (or title/publication if author is unknown) for each source. Then briefly summarize the key points of that source.

Here, point out any flaws with your most relevant sources, then note any gaps between these same sources.

Intro Sketch

Based on this research, your own thinking and observations, what is your hypothesis, or proposal?

Why is your proposal important? Who or what does it affect? How does it affect them?

Body Outline

Here you will sketch a loose outline of your content. Summarize all of your assertions, and whatever support you have for that assertion. Acknowledge gaps in your argument, and respond to the arguments of others. Also consider whether your assumptions about the subject area will be contentious or unexpected to your reader.

ASSERTION
SUPPORT
    CONTENTIOUS?
    UNEXPECTED?

ASSERTION
SUPPORT
    CONTENTIOUS?
    UNEXPECTED?

ASSERTION
SUPPORT
    CONTENTIOUS?
    UNEXPECTED?

ASSERTION
SUPPORT
    CONTENTIOUS?
    UNEXPECTED?

ASSERTION
SUPPORT
    CONTENTIOUS?
    UNEXPECTED?

ASSERTION
SUPPORT
    CONTENTIOUS?
    UNEXPECTED?

Body Outline

Imagine the progression, or organization, of your final draft. Is your argument best organized chronologically, topically, or by association? **Using the circles provided**, reorder the sections by writing an order number in the circles provided. When you write the first draft you will use this new order, and each item should be at least one paragraph.

 ASSERTION
SUPPORT
    CONTENTIOUS?
    UNEXPECTED?

 ASSERTION
SUPPORT
    CONTENTIOUS?
    UNEXPECTED?

 ASSERTION
SUPPORT
    CONTENTIOUS?
    UNEXPECTED?

 ASSERTION
SUPPORT
    CONTENTIOUS?
    UNEXPECTED?

 ASSERTION
SUPPORT
    CONTENTIOUS?
    UNEXPECTED?

 ASSERTION
SUPPORT
    CONTENTIOUS?
    UNEXPECTED?

Intro Rewrite

Here you will rework your introduction by adding an opening. Consider a "hook" that helps develop context and draw interest, and empathize with your reader's position. Connect this hook to the greater signficance of your argument. Finish by offering a proposition.

Opening.

Proposal.

Context.

Your research.

Conclusion and Title

Here you can write a conclusion that brings some kind of closure to your argument, while at the same time offering additional significance, or importance, and making a specific call for additional research beyond what you've written in this essay, making plain the potential opportunities for future inquiry (not addressed by this essay). Start with a general closing that echoes, but does not copy, your introduction.

Closing.

Proposal.

Significance.

Additional research that should be done.

Conclusion and Title

WHAT'S YOUR TITLE?
Your title should be specific to your proposal.

Assignment:

Instructor:

Course:

Due Date:

	Due Date(s)
Specifications	24
Reader Expectations	26
APA	28
MLA	29
Source Analysis	30
Intro Sketch	38

Specifications

Will you be using a style guide, such as MLA, APA? If so, which. Also note any exceptions or special requirements you have for this essay.

What particular font, margin, and spacing requirements do you need?

Do you need a minimum number of sources?

Do you need peer reviewed sources?

Do you need primary sources, secondary sources, or both?

Do you need to reference one or more course texts? If so which texts, and and what chapters, pages, parts, or aspects should you reference?

Is there a minimum length the final draft should attain? If so, what is it?

Specifications

Are there additional materials required outside of those marked already in these specifications?

Will you be submitting the final draft by email, hardcopy, upload, or something else? Describe exactly how you will submit your final work.

How many drafts are due, and when are they due? List all of the drafts below, and their respective due dates.

Reader Expectations

MY READER CAN BE DESCRIBED AS...

Readers can generally be categorized as professionals, well informed general public, or ill-informed general public. Consider which of these broad categories your ideal reader falls into. Does the reader expect to be entertained, provided with new knowledge, or helped to solve a practical problem? **Choose only one.**

EXPERT
- ☐ Provided with knowledge
- ☐ Helped to solve a practical problem
- ☐ Entertained

GENERAL PUBLIC
- ☐ Provided with knowledge
- ☐ Helped to solve a practical problem
- ☐ Entertained

POLICY MAKER
- ☐ Provided with knowledge
- ☐ Helped to solve a practical problem
- ☐ Entertained

OTHER
- ☐ Provided with knowledge
- ☐ Helped to solve a practical problem
- ☐ Entertained

WHAT'S MY READER'S PERSPECTIVE?

Essays must generally make some kind of proposal. Does your proposal solve a problem that your ideal reader would recognize? Or might the proposal itself represent a new problem to them? If your ideal reader is unlikely to understand with or agree with your proposal, they may need to be convinced.

- ☐ The problem is already recognized by reader.
- ☐ The problem would be new to the reader.
- ☐ The reader sees no problem at all.

HOW WILL MY READER REACT?

Does your proposal contradict what the reader believes, and if so, how? Can you anticipate their response? Will showing the reader the steps that led you to your proposition convince them?

Reader Expectations

A P A

APA: make sure to list the sources alphabetically by their first entry.

APA

Doe, J.A., & Doe, J.B. (Year). Title of source. Title of Publication, volume number (if available), pages referenced, http://dx.doi.org/xx.xxx/yyyyy.

MLA

MLA: 8th Edition MLA works cited entries use a "container" metaphor; an article is contained within a newspaper; a chapter is contained within a book; an episode is contained within a series. There can be containers within containers (for example an article within a journal within a database). Location always refers to the location of the source within its container (for example, pp. 50-55). Use Version and Number only for periodicals (like academic journals and magazines); the edition is always part of the title. Make sure to list the sources by their first entry alphabetically.

MLA

Doe, Jane A., and John B. Doe. "Title of Source." Container. Contributers, Version, Number, Publisher, Publication Date, Location. Second Container. Publisher, Publication Date, Location.

Source Analysis

Is the research current, and if not, what is the historical context in which it was produced? What is the general history of this document? Who are the original contributer(s) and author(s)? What other forces have shaped it, political, economic, or otherwise?

SOURCE CHECKLIST

☐ Authored by a scholar:
  ☐ Authored by an expert:
  ☐ Authored by an organization:
  ☐ Unknown author
☐ Published
  ☐ by a university press:
  ☐ by another press:
  ☐ Sponsored by an organization:
☐ Primary Source
  ☐ Secondary Source
  ☐ Tertiary Source
☐ Current
  ☐ Historical Document
☐ Peer-reviewed by:
  ☐ Critically reviewed by:
  ☐ Cited by:
☐ Contains a bibliography
☐ Contains keywords
☐ Contains good quotes
☐ Connects to my argument
☐ Contradicts my argument

How does it support your argument? Explain how it supports your argument.

How does it contradict your argument? Paraphrase or use direct quote and explain the contradiction.

Promising entries from the source's bibliography:

Who is the author? What are the author's credentials? What else has the author written? What is their stance on, or interest in, the topic?

Briefly summarize the source here.

Who is the publisher? What is the publisher's editorial policy? Is the publisher an imprint owned by another company, a website run by a government agency, or a private blog? What is the purpose, or mission, of the publisher?

Source Checklist

- ☐ Authored by a scholar:
  - ☐ Authored by an expert:
  - ☐ Authored by an organization:
  - ☐ Unknown author
- ☐ Published
  - ☐ by a university press:
  - ☐ by another press:
  - ☐ Sponsored by an organization:
- ☐ Primary Source
  - ☐ Secondary Source
  - ☐ Tertiary Source
- ☐ Current
  - ☐ Historical Document
- ☐ Peer-reviewed by:
  - ☐ Critically reviewed by:
  - ☐ Cited by:
- ☐ Contains a bibliography
- ☐ Contains keywords
- ☐ Contains good quotes
- ☐ Connects to my argument
- ☐ Contradicts my argument

Is the research current, and if not, what is the historical context in which it was produced? What is the general history of this document? Who are the original contributer(s) and author(s)? What other forces have shaped it, political, economic, or otherwise?

How does it support your argument? Explain how it supports your argument.

How does it contradict your argument? Paraphrase or use direct quote and explain the contradiction.

Promising entries from the source's bibliography:

Who is the author? What are the author's credentials? What else has the author written? What is their stance on, or interest in, the topic?

Briefly summarize the source here.

Who is the publisher? What is the publisher's editorial policy? Is the publisher an imprint owned by another company, a website run by a government agency, or a private blog? What is the purpose, or mission, of the publisher?

Source Checklist

- ☐ Authored by a scholar:
  - ☐ Authored by an expert:
  - ☐ Authored by an organization:
  - ☐ Unknown author
- ☐ Published
  - ☐ by a university press:
  - ☐ by another press:
  - ☐ Sponsored by an organization:
- ☐ Primary Source
  - ☐ Secondary Source
  - ☐ Tertiary Source
- ☐ Current
  - ☐ Historical Document
- ☐ Peer-reviewed by:
  - ☐ Critically reviewed by:
  - ☐ Cited by:
- ☐ Contains a bibliography
- ☐ Contains keywords
- ☐ Contains good quotes
- ☐ Connects to my argument
- ☐ Contradicts my argument

Is the research current, and if not, what is the historical context in which it was produced? What is the general history of this document? Who are the original contributer(s) and author(s)? What other forces have shaped it, political, economic, or otherwise?

How does it support your argument? Explain how it supports your argument.

How does it contradict your argument? Paraphrase or use direct quote and explain the contradiction.

Promising entries from the source's bibliography:

Who is the author? What are the author's credentials? What else has the author written? What is their stance on, or interest in, the topic?

Briefly summarize the source here.

Who is the publisher? What is the publisher's editorial policy? Is the publisher an imprint owned by another company, a website run by a government agency, or a private blog? What is the purpose, or mission, of the publisher?

Source Checklist

- ☐ Authored by a scholar:
  - ☐ Authored by an expert:
  - ☐ Authored by an organization:
  - ☐ Unknown author
- ☐ Published
  - ☐ by a university press:
  - ☐ by another press:
  - ☐ Sponsored by an organization:
- ☐ Primary Source
  - ☐ Secondary Source
  - ☐ Tertiary Source
- ☐ Current
  - ☐ Historical Document
- ☐ Peer-reviewed by:
  - ☐ Critically reviewed by:
  - ☐ Cited by:
- ☐ Contains a bibliography
- ☐ Contains keywords
- ☐ Contains good quotes
- ☐ Connects to my argument
- ☐ Contradicts my argument

Is the research current, and if not, what is the historical context in which it was produced? What is the general history of this document? Who are the original contributer(s) and author(s)? What other forces have shaped it, political, economic, or otherwise?

How does it support your argument? Explain how it supports your argument.

How does it contradict your argument? Paraphrase or use direct quote and explain the contradiction.

Promising entries from the source's bibliography:

Who is the author? What are the author's credentials? What else has the author written? What is their stance on, or interest in, the topic?

Briefly summarize the source here.

Who is the publisher? What is the publisher's editorial policy? Is the publisher an imprint owned by another company, a website run by a government agency, or a private blog? What is the purpose, or mission, of the publisher?

SOURCE CHECKLIST

- ☐ Authored by a scholar:
  - ☐ Authored by an expert:
  - ☐ Authored by an organization:
  - ☐ Unknown author
- ☐ Published
  - ☐ by a university press:
  - ☐ by another press:
  - ☐ Sponsored by an organization:
- ☐ Primary Source
  - ☐ Secondary Source
  - ☐ Tertiary Source
- ☐ Current
  - ☐ Historical Document
- ☐ Peer-reviewed by:
  - ☐ Critically reviewed by:
  - ☐ Cited by:
- ☐ Contains a bibliography
- ☐ Contains keywords
- ☐ Contains good quotes
- ☐ Connects to my argument
- ☐ Contradicts my argument

Is the research current, and if not, what is the historical context in which it was produced? What is the general history of this document? Who are the original contributer(s) and author(s)? What other forces have shaped it, political, economic, or otherwise?

How does it support your argument? Explain how it supports your argument.

How does it contradict your argument? Paraphrase or use direct quote and explain the contradiction.

Promising entries from the source's bibliography:

Who is the author? What are the author's credentials? What else has the author written? What is their stance on, or interest in, the topic?

Briefly summarize the source here.

Who is the publisher? What is the publisher's editorial policy? Is the publisher an imprint owned by another company, a website run by a government agency, or a private blog? What is the purpose, or mission, of the publisher?

Source Checklist

- ☐ Authored by a scholar:
  - ☐ Authored by an expert:
  - ☐ Authored by an organization:
  - ☐ Unknown author
- ☐ Published
  - ☐ by a university press:
  - ☐ by another press:
  - ☐ Sponsored by an organization:
- ☐ Primary Source
  - ☐ Secondary Source
  - ☐ Tertiary Source
- ☐ Current
  - ☐ Historical Document
- ☐ Peer-reviewed by:
  - ☐ Critically reviewed by:
  - ☐ Cited by:
- ☐ Contains a bibliography
- ☐ Contains keywords
- ☐ Contains good quotes
- ☐ Connects to my argument
- ☐ Contradicts my argument

Is the research current, and if not, what is the historical context in which it was produced? What is the general history of this document? Who are the original contributer(s) and author(s)? What other forces have shaped it, political, economic, or otherwise?

How does it support your argument? Explain how it supports your argument.

How does it contradict your argument? Paraphrase or use direct quote and explain the contradiction.

Promising entries from the source's bibliography:

Who is the author? What are the author's credentials? What else has the author written? What is their stance on, or interest in, the topic?

Briefly summarize the source here.

Who is the publisher? What is the publisher's editorial policy? Is the publisher an imprint owned by another company, a website run by a government agency, or a private blog? What is the purpose, or mission, of the publisher?

SOURCE CHECKLIST

- ☐ Authored by a scholar:
  - ☐ Authored by an expert:
  - ☐ Authored by an organization:
  - ☐ Unknown author
- ☐ Published
  - ☐ by a university press:
  - ☐ by another press:
  - ☐ Sponsored by an organization:
- ☐ Primary Source
  - ☐ Secondary Source
  - ☐ Tertiary Source
- ☐ Current
  - ☐ Historical Document
- ☐ Peer-reviewed by:
  - ☐ Critically reviewed by:
  - ☐ Cited by:
- ☐ Contains a bibliography
- ☐ Contains keywords
- ☐ Contains good quotes
- ☐ Connects to my argument
- ☐ Contradicts my argument

Is the research current, and if not, what is the historical context in which it was produced? What is the general history of this document? Who are the original contributer(s) and author(s)? What other forces have shaped it, political, economic, or otherwise?

How does it support your argument? Explain how it supports your argument.

How does it contradict your argument? Paraphrase or use direct quote and explain the contradiction.

Promising entries from the source's bibliography:

Who is the author? What are the author's credentials? What else has the author written? What is their stance on, or interest in, the topic?

Briefly summarize the source here.

Who is the publisher? What is the publisher's editorial policy? Is the publisher an imprint owned by another company, a website run by a government agency, or a private blog? What is the purpose, or mission, of the publisher?

SOURCE CHECKLIST

- ☐ Authored by a scholar:
  - ☐ Authored by an expert:
  - ☐ Authored by an organization:
  - ☐ Unknown author
- ☐ Published
  - ☐ by a university press:
  - ☐ by another press:
  - ☐ Sponsored by an organization:
- ☐ Primary Source
  - ☐ Secondary Source
  - ☐ Tertiary Source
- ☐ Current
  - ☐ Historical Document
- ☐ Peer-reviewed by:
  - ☐ Critically reviewed by:
  - ☐ Cited by:
- ☐ Contains a bibliography
- ☐ Contains keywords
- ☐ Contains good quotes
- ☐ Connects to my argument
- ☐ Contradicts my argument

Is the research current, and if not, what is the historical context in which it was produced? What is the general history of this document? Who are the original contributer(s) and author(s)? What other forces have shaped it, political, economic, or otherwise?

How does it support your argument? Explain how it supports your argument.

How does it contradict your argument? Paraphrase or use direct quote and explain the contradiction.

Promising entries from the source's bibliography:

Who is the author? What are the author's credentials? What else has the author written? What is their stance on, or interest in, the topic?

Briefly summarize the source here.

Who is the publisher? What is the publisher's editorial policy? Is the publisher an imprint owned by another company, a website run by a government agency, or a private blog? What is the purpose, or mission, of the publisher?

Intro Sketch

List your most relevant sources. Write the last name (or title/publication if author is unknown) for each source. Then briefly summarize the key points of that source.

Here, point out any flaws with your most relevant sources, then note any gaps between these same sources.

Intro Sketch

Based on this research, your own thinking and observations, what is your
hypothesis, or proposal?

Why is your proposal important? Who or what does it affect? How does it affect
them?

Body Outline

Here you will sketch a loose outline of your content. Summarize all of your assertions, and whatever support you have for that assertion. Acknowledge gaps in your argument, and respond to the arguments of others. Also consider whether your assumptions about the subject area will be contentious or unexpected to your reader.

ASSERTION
SUPPORT
    CONTENTIOUS?
    UNEXPECTED?

ASSERTION
SUPPORT
    CONTENTIOUS?
    UNEXPECTED?

ASSERTION
SUPPORT
    CONTENTIOUS?
    UNEXPECTED?

ASSERTION
SUPPORT
    CONTENTIOUS?
    UNEXPECTED?

ASSERTION
SUPPORT
    CONTENTIOUS?
    UNEXPECTED?

ASSERTION
SUPPORT
    CONTENTIOUS?
    UNEXPECTED?

Body Outline

Imagine the progression, or organization, of your final draft. Is your argument best organized chronologically, topically, or by association? **Using the circles provided**, reorder the sections by writing an order number in the circles provided. When you write the first draft you will use this new order, and each item should be at least one paragraph.

ASSERTION

SUPPORT

    CONTENTIOUS?

    UNEXPECTED?

ASSERTION

SUPPORT

    CONTENTIOUS?

    UNEXPECTED?

ASSERTION

SUPPORT

    CONTENTIOUS?

    UNEXPECTED?

ASSERTION

SUPPORT

    CONTENTIOUS?

    UNEXPECTED?

ASSERTION

SUPPORT

    CONTENTIOUS?

    UNEXPECTED?

ASSERTION

SUPPORT

    CONTENTIOUS?

    UNEXPECTED?

Intro Rewrite

Here you will rework your introduction by adding an opening. Consider a "hook" that helps develop context and draw interest, and empathize with your reader's position. Connect this hook to the greater signficance of your argument. Finish by offering a proposition.

Opening.

Proposal.

Context.

Your research.

Conclusion and Title

Here you can write a conclusion that brings some kind of closure to your argument, while at the same time offering additional significance, or importance, and making a specific call for additional research beyond what you've written in this essay, making plain the potential opportunities for future inquiry (not addressed by this essay). Start with a general closing that echoes, but does not copy, your introduction.

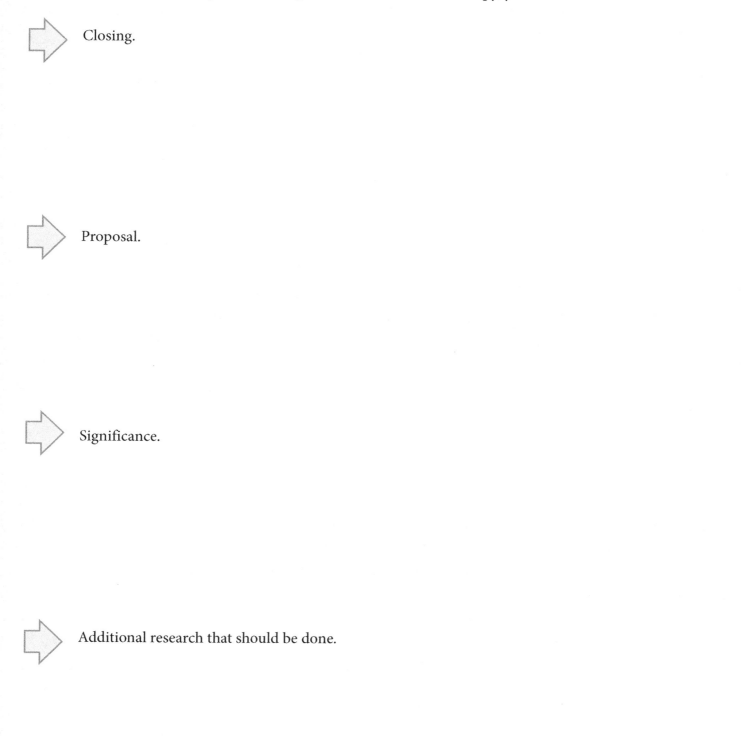

Closing.

Proposal.

Significance.

Additional research that should be done.

Conclusion and Title

WHAT'S YOUR TITLE?
Your title should be specific to your proposal.

Assignment:

Instructor:

Course:

Due Date:

		Due Date(s)
Specifications	46	
Reader Expectations	48	
APA	50	
MLA	51	
Source Analysis	52	
Intro Sketch	60	

Specifications

Will you be using a style guide, such as MLA, APA? If so, which. Also note any exceptions or special requirements you have for this essay.

What particular font, margin, and spacing requirements do you need?

Do you need a minimum number of sources?

Do you need peer reviewed sources?

Do you need primary sources, secondary sources, or both?

Do you need to reference one or more course texts? If so which texts, and and what chapters, pages, parts, or aspects should you reference?

Is there a minimum length the final draft should attain? If so, what is it?

Specifications

Are there additional materials required outside of those marked already in these specifications?

Will you be submitting the final draft by email, hardcopy, upload, or something else? Describe exactly how you will submit your final work.

How many drafts are due, and when are they due? List all of the drafts below, and their respective due dates.

Reader Expectations

MY READER CAN BE DESCRIBED AS...

Readers can generally be categorized as professionals, well informed general public, or ill-informed general public. Consider which of these broad categories your ideal reader falls into. Does the reader expect to be entertained, provided with new knowledge, or helped to solve a practical problem? **Choose only one.**

EXPERT

☐ Provided with knowledge

☐ Helped to solve a practical problem

☐ Entertained

GENERAL PUBLIC

☐ Provided with knowledge

☐ Helped to solve a practical problem

☐ Entertained

POLICY MAKER

☐ Provided with knowledge

☐ Helped to solve a practical problem

☐ Entertained

OTHER

☐ Provided with knowledge

☐ Helped to solve a practical problem

☐ Entertained

WHAT'S MY READER'S PERSPECTIVE?

Essays must generally make some kind of proposal. Does your proposal solve a problem that your ideal reader would recognize? Or might the proposal itself represent a new problem to them? If your ideal reader is unlikely to understand with or agree with your proposal, they may need to be convinced.

☐ The problem is already recognized by reader.

☐ The problem would be new to the reader.

☐ The reader sees no problem at all.

HOW WILL MY READER REACT?

Does your proposal contradict what the reader believes, and if so, how? Can you anticipate their response? Will showing the reader the steps that led you to your proposition convince them?

Reader Expectations

A P A

APA: make sure to list the sources alphabetically by their first entry.

APA

Doe, J.A., & Doe, J.B. (Year). Title of source. Title of Publication, volume number (if available), pages referenced, http://dx.doi.org/xx.xxx/yyyyy.

M L A

MLA: 8th Edition MLA works cited entries use a "container" metaphor; an article is contained within a newspaper; a chapter is contained within a book; an episode is contained within a series. There can be containers within containers (for example an article within a journal within a database). Location always refers to the location of the source within its container (for example, pp. 50-55). Use Version and Number only for periodicals (like academic journals and magazines); the edition is always part of the title. Make sure to list the sources by their first entry alphabetically.

MLA

Doe, Jane A., and John B. Doe. "Title of Source." Container. Contributers, Version, Number, Publisher, Publication Date, Location. Second Container. Publisher, Publication Date, Location.

Source Analysis

Source Checklist

- ☐ Authored by a scholar:
    - ☐ Authored by an expert:
    - ☐ Authored by an organization:
    - ☐ Unknown author
- ☐ Published
    - ☐ by a university press:
    - ☐ by another press:
    - ☐ Sponsored by an organization:
- ☐ Primary Source
    - ☐ Secondary Source
    - ☐ Tertiary Source
- ☐ Current
    - ☐ Historical Document
- ☐ Peer-reviewed by:
    - ☐ Critically reviewed by:
    - ☐ Cited by:
- ☐ Contains a bibliography
- ☐ Contains keywords
- ☐ Contains good quotes
- ☐ Connects to my argument
- ☐ Contradicts my argument

Is the research current, and if not, what is the historical context in which it was produced? What is the general history of this document? Who are the original contributer(s) and author(s)? What other forces have shaped it, political, economic, or otherwise?

How does it support your argument? Explain how it supports your argument.

How does it contradict your argument? Paraphrase or use direct quote and explain the contradiction.

Promising entries from the source's bibliography:

Who is the author? What are the author's credentials? What else has the author written? What is their stance on, or interest in, the topic?

Briefly summarize the source here.

Who is the publisher? What is the publisher's editorial policy? Is the publisher an imprint owned by another company, a website run by a government agency, or a private blog? What is the purpose, or mission, of the publisher?

Source Checklist

- ☐ Authored by a scholar:
  - ☐ Authored by an expert:
  - ☐ Authored by an organization:
  - ☐ Unknown author
- ☐ Published
  - ☐ by a university press:
  - ☐ by another press:
  - ☐ Sponsored by an organization:
- ☐ Primary Source
  - ☐ Secondary Source
  - ☐ Tertiary Source
- ☐ Current
  - ☐ Historical Document
- ☐ Peer-reviewed by:
  - ☐ Critically reviewed by:
  - ☐ Cited by:
- ☐ Contains a bibliography
- ☐ Contains keywords
- ☐ Contains good quotes
- ☐ Connects to my argument
- ☐ Contradicts my argument

Is the research current, and if not, what is the historical context in which it was produced? What is the general history of this document? Who are the original contributer(s) and author(s)? What other forces have shaped it, political, economic, or otherwise?

How does it support your argument? Explain how it supports your argument.

How does it contradict your argument? Paraphrase or use direct quote and explain the contradiction.

Promising entries from the source's bibliography:

Who is the author? What are the author's credentials? What else has the author written? What is their stance on, or interest in, the topic?

Briefly summarize the source here.

Who is the publisher? What is the publisher's editorial policy? Is the publisher an imprint owned by another company, a website run by a government agency, or a private blog? What is the purpose, or mission, of the publisher?

SOURCE CHECKLIST

- ☐ Authored by a scholar:
  - ☐ Authored by an expert:
  - ☐ Authored by an organization:
  - ☐ Unknown author
- ☐ Published
  - ☐ by a university press:
  - ☐ by another press:
  - ☐ Sponsored by an organization:
- ☐ Primary Source
  - ☐ Secondary Source
  - ☐ Tertiary Source
- ☐ Current
  - ☐ Historical Document
- ☐ Peer-reviewed by:
  - ☐ Critically reviewed by:
  - ☐ Cited by:
- ☐ Contains a bibliography
- ☐ Contains keywords
- ☐ Contains good quotes
- ☐ Connects to my argument
- ☐ Contradicts my argument

Is the research current, and if not, what is the historical context in which it was produced? What is the general history of this document? Who are the original contributer(s) and author(s)? What other forces have shaped it, political, economic, or otherwise?

How does it support your argument? Explain how it supports your argument.

How does it contradict your argument? Paraphrase or use direct quote and explain the contradiction.

Promising entries from the source's bibliography:

Who is the author? What are the author's credentials? What else has the author written? What is their stance on, or interest in, the topic?

Briefly summarize the source here.

Who is the publisher? What is the publisher's editorial policy? Is the publisher an imprint owned by another company, a website run by a government agency, or a private blog? What is the purpose, or mission, of the publisher?

Source Checklist

- ☐ Authored by a scholar:
  - ☐ Authored by an expert:
  - ☐ Authored by an organization:
  - ☐ Unknown author
- ☐ Published
  - ☐ by a university press:
  - ☐ by another press:
  - ☐ Sponsored by an organization:
- ☐ Primary Source
  - ☐ Secondary Source
  - ☐ Tertiary Source
- ☐ Current
  - ☐ Historical Document
- ☐ Peer-reviewed by:
  - ☐ Critically reviewed by:
  - ☐ Cited by:
- ☐ Contains a bibliography
- ☐ Contains keywords
- ☐ Contains good quotes
- ☐ Connects to my argument
- ☐ Contradicts my argument

Is the research current, and if not, what is the historical context in which it was produced? What is the general history of this document? Who are the original contributer(s) and author(s)? What other forces have shaped it, political, economic, or otherwise?

How does it support your argument? Explain how it supports your argument.

How does it contradict your argument? Paraphrase or use direct quote and explain the contradiction.

Promising entries from the source's bibliography:

Who is the author? What are the author's credentials? What else has the author written? What is their stance on, or interest in, the topic?

Briefly summarize the source here.

Who is the publisher? What is the publisher's editorial policy? Is the publisher an imprint owned by another company, a website run by a government agency, or a private blog? What is the purpose, or mission, of the publisher?

SOURCE CHECKLIST

- ☐ Authored by a scholar:
  - ☐ Authored by an expert:
  - ☐ Authored by an organization:
  - ☐ Unknown author
- ☐ Published
  - ☐ by a university press:
  - ☐ by another press:
  - ☐ Sponsored by an organization:
- ☐ Primary Source
  - ☐ Secondary Source
  - ☐ Tertiary Source
- ☐ Current
  - ☐ Historical Document
- ☐ Peer-reviewed by:
  - ☐ Critically reviewed by:
  - ☐ Cited by:
- ☐ Contains a bibliography
- ☐ Contains keywords
- ☐ Contains good quotes
- ☐ Connects to my argument
- ☐ Contradicts my argument

Is the research current, and if not, what is the historical context in which it was produced? What is the general history of this document? Who are the original contributer(s) and author(s)? What other forces have shaped it, political, economic, or otherwise?

How does it support your argument? Explain how it supports your argument.

How does it contradict your argument? Paraphrase or use direct quote and explain the contradiction.

Promising entries from the source's bibliography:

Who is the author? What are the author's credentials? What else has the author written? What is their stance on, or interest in, the topic?

Briefly summarize the source here.

Who is the publisher? What is the publisher's editorial policy? Is the publisher an imprint owned by another company, a website run by a government agency, or a private blog? What is the purpose, or mission, of the publisher?

SOURCE CHECKLIST

- ☐ Authored by a scholar:
  - ☐ Authored by an expert:
  - ☐ Authored by an organization:
  - ☐ Unknown author
- ☐ Published
  - ☐ by a university press:
  - ☐ by another press:
  - ☐ Sponsored by an organization:
- ☐ Primary Source
  - ☐ Secondary Source
  - ☐ Tertiary Source
- ☐ Current
  - ☐ Historical Document
- ☐ Peer-reviewed by:
  - ☐ Critically reviewed by:
  - ☐ Cited by:
- ☐ Contains a bibliography
- ☐ Contains keywords
- ☐ Contains good quotes
- ☐ Connects to my argument
- ☐ Contradicts my argument

Is the research current, and if not, what is the historical context in which it was produced? What is the general history of this document? Who are the original contributer(s) and author(s)? What other forces have shaped it, political, economic, or otherwise?

How does it support your argument? Explain how it supports your argument.

How does it contradict your argument? Paraphrase or use direct quote and explain the contradiction.

Promising entries from the source's bibliography:

Who is the author? What are the author's credentials? What else has the author written? What is their stance on, or interest in, the topic?

Briefly summarize the source here.

Who is the publisher? What is the publisher's editorial policy? Is the publisher an imprint owned by another company, a website run by a government agency, or a private blog? What is the purpose, or mission, of the publisher?

Source Checklist

- ☐ Authored by a scholar:
  - ☐ Authored by an expert:
  - ☐ Authored by an organization:
  - ☐ Unknown author
- ☐ Published
  - ☐ by a university press:
  - ☐ by another press:
  - ☐ Sponsored by an organization:
- ☐ Primary Source
  - ☐ Secondary Source
  - ☐ Tertiary Source
- ☐ Current
  - ☐ Historical Document
- ☐ Peer-reviewed by:
  - ☐ Critically reviewed by:
  - ☐ Cited by:
- ☐ Contains a bibliography
- ☐ Contains keywords
- ☐ Contains good quotes
- ☐ Connects to my argument
- ☐ Contradicts my argument

Is the research current, and if not, what is the historical context in which it was produced? What is the general history of this document? Who are the original contributer(s) and author(s)? What other forces have shaped it, political, economic, or otherwise?

How does it support your argument? Explain how it supports your argument.

How does it contradict your argument? Paraphrase or use direct quote and explain the contradiction.

Promising entries from the source's bibliography:

Briefly summarize the source here.

Who is the author? What are the author's credentials? What else has the author written? What is their stance on, or interest in, the topic?

Who is the publisher? What is the publisher's editorial policy? Is the publisher an imprint owned by another company, a website run by a government agency, or a private blog? What is the purpose, or mission, of the publisher?

Source Checklist

- ☐ Authored by a scholar:
  - ☐ Authored by an expert:
  - ☐ Authored by an organization:
  - ☐ Unknown author
- ☐ Published
  - ☐ by a university press:
  - ☐ by another press:
  - ☐ Sponsored by an organization:
- ☐ Primary Source
  - ☐ Secondary Source
  - ☐ Tertiary Source
- ☐ Current
  - ☐ Historical Document
- ☐ Peer-reviewed by:
  - ☐ Critically reviewed by:
  - ☐ Cited by:
- ☐ Contains a bibliography
- ☐ Contains keywords
- ☐ Contains good quotes
- ☐ Connects to my argument
- ☐ Contradicts my argument

Is the research current, and if not, what is the historical context in which it was produced? What is the general history of this document? Who are the original contributer(s) and author(s)? What other forces have shaped it, political, economic, or otherwise?

How does it support your argument? Explain how it supports your argument.

How does it contradict your argument? Paraphrase or use direct quote and explain the contradiction.

Promising entries from the source's bibliography:

Who is the author? What are the author's credentials? What else has the author written? What is their stance on, or interest in, the topic?

Briefly summarize the source here.

Who is the publisher? What is the publisher's editorial policy? Is the publisher an imprint owned by another company, a website run by a government agency, or a private blog? What is the purpose, or mission, of the publisher?

Intro Sketch

List your most relevant sources. Write the last name (or title/publication if author is unknown) for each source. Then briefly summarize the key points of that source.

Here, point out any flaws with your most relevant sources, then note any gaps between these same sources.

Intro Sketch

Based on this research, your own thinking and observations, what is your
hypothesis, or proposal?

Why is your proposal important? Who or what does it affect? How does it affect
them?

Body Outline

Here you will sketch a loose outline of your content. Summarize all of your assertions, and whatever support you have for that assertion. Acknowledge gaps in your argument, and respond to the arguments of others. Also consider whether your assumptions about the subject area will be contentious or unexpected to your reader.

ASSERTION
SUPPORT
   CONTENTIOUS?
   UNEXPECTED?

ASSERTION
SUPPORT
   CONTENTIOUS?
   UNEXPECTED?

ASSERTION
SUPPORT
   CONTENTIOUS?
   UNEXPECTED?

ASSERTION
SUPPORT
   CONTENTIOUS?
   UNEXPECTED?

ASSERTION
SUPPORT
   CONTENTIOUS?
   UNEXPECTED?

ASSERTION
SUPPORT
   CONTENTIOUS?
   UNEXPECTED?

Body Outline

Imagine the progression, or organization, of your final draft. Is your argument best organized chronologically, topically, or by association? **Using the circles provided**, reorder the sections by writing an order number in the circles provided. When you write the first draft you will use this new order, and each item should be at least one paragraph.

ASSERTION
SUPPORT
    CONTENTIOUS?
    UNEXPECTED?

ASSERTION
SUPPORT
    CONTENTIOUS?
    UNEXPECTED?

ASSERTION
SUPPORT
    CONTENTIOUS?
    UNEXPECTED?

ASSERTION
SUPPORT
    CONTENTIOUS?
    UNEXPECTED?

ASSERTION
SUPPORT
    CONTENTIOUS?
    UNEXPECTED?

ASSERTION
SUPPORT
    CONTENTIOUS?
    UNEXPECTED?

Intro Rewrite

Here you will rework your introduction by adding an opening. Consider a "hook" that helps develop context and draw interest, and empathize with your reader's position. Connect this hook to the greater signficance of your argument. Finish by offering a proposition.

Opening.

Proposal.

Context.

Your research.

Conclusion and Title

Here you can write a conclusion that brings some kind of closure to your argument, while at the same time offering additional significance, or importance, and making a specific call for additional research beyond what you've written in this essay, making plain the potential opportunities for future inquiry (not addressed by this essay). Start with a general closing that echoes, but does not copy, your introduction.

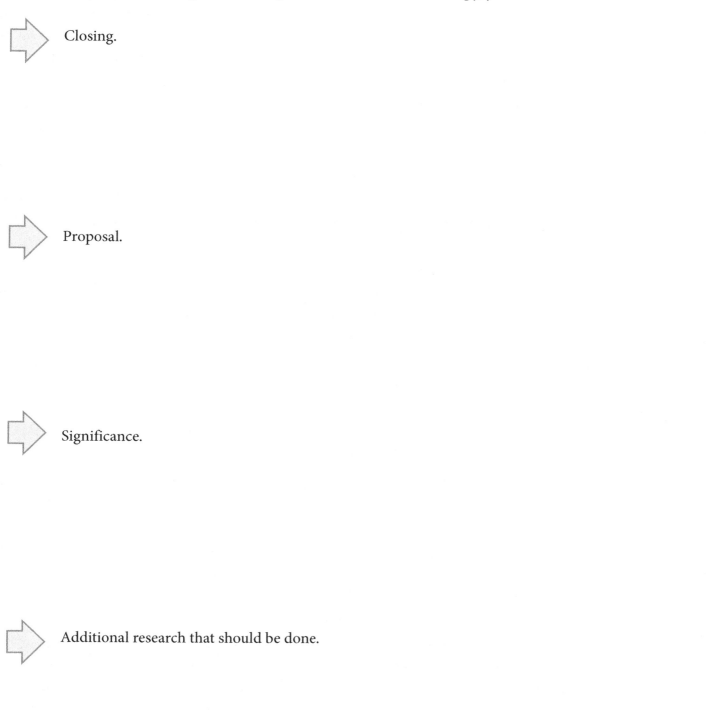

Closing.

Proposal.

Significance.

Additional research that should be done.

Conclusion and Title

WHAT'S YOUR TITLE?
Your title should be specific to your proposal.

Assignment:

Instructor:

Course:

Due Date:

		Due Date(s)
Specifications	68	
Reader Expectations	70	
APA	72	
MLA	73	
Source Analysis	74	
Intro Sketch	82	

Specifications

Will you be using a style guide, such as MLA, APA? If so, which. Also note any exceptions or special requirements you have for this essay.

What particular font, margin, and spacing requirements do you need?

Do you need a minimum number of sources?

Do you need peer reviewed sources?

Do you need primary sources, secondary sources, or both?

Do you need to reference one or more course texts? If so which texts, and and what chapters, pages, parts, or aspects should you reference?

Is there a minimum length the final draft should attain? If so, what is it?

Specifications

Are there additional materials required outside of those marked already in these specifications?

Will you be submitting the final draft by email, hardcopy, upload, or something else? Describe exactly how you will submit your final work.

How many drafts are due, and when are they due? List all of the drafts below, and their respective due dates.

Reader Expectations

MY READER CAN BE DESCRIBED AS...

Readers can generally be categorized as professionals, well informed general public, or ill-informed general public. Consider which of these broad categories your ideal reader falls into. Does the reader expect to be entertained, provided with new knowledge, or helped to solve a practical problem? **Choose only one.**

EXPERT
- ☐ Provided with knowledge
- ☐ Helped to solve a practical problem
- ☐ Entertained

GENERAL PUBLIC
- ☐ Provided with knowledge
- ☐ Helped to solve a practical problem
- ☐ Entertained

POLICY MAKER
- ☐ Provided with knowledge
- ☐ Helped to solve a practical problem
- ☐ Entertained

OTHER
- ☐ Provided with knowledge
- ☐ Helped to solve a practical problem
- ☐ Entertained

WHAT'S MY READER'S PERSPECTIVE?

Essays must generally make some kind of proposal. Does your proposal solve a problem that your ideal reader would recognize? Or might the proposal itself represent a new problem to them? If your ideal reader is unlikely to understand with or agree with your proposal, they may need to be convinced.

- ☐ The problem is already recognized by reader.
- ☐ The problem would be new to the reader.
- ☐ The reader sees no problem at all.

HOW WILL MY READER REACT?

Does your proposal contradict what the reader believes, and if so, how? Can you anticipate their response? Will showing the reader the steps that led you to your proposition convince them?

Reader Expectations

A P A

APA: make sure to list the sources alphabetically by their first entry.

APA

Doe, J.A., & Doe, J.B. (Year). Title of source. Title of Publication, volume number (if available), pages referenced, http://dx.doi.org/xx.xxx/yyyyy.

M L A

MLA: 8th Edition MLA works cited entries use a "container" metaphor; an article is contained within a newspaper; a chapter is contained within a book; an episode is contained within a series. There can be containers within containers (for example an article within a journal within a database). Location always refers to the location of the source within its container (for example, pp. 50-55). Use Version and Number only for periodicals (like academic journals and magazines); the edition is always part of the title. Make sure to list the sources by their first entry alphabetically.

MLA

Doe, Jane A., and John B. Doe. "Title of Source." Container. Contributers, Version, Number, Publisher, Publication Date, Location. Second Container. Publisher, Publication Date, Location.

Source Analysis

SOURCE CHECKLIST

- ☐ Authored by a scholar:
  - ☐ Authored by an expert:
  - ☐ Authored by an organization:
  - ☐ Unknown author
- ☐ Published
  - ☐ by a university press:
  - ☐ by another press:
  - ☐ Sponsored by an organization:
- ☐ Primary Source
  - ☐ Secondary Source
  - ☐ Tertiary Source
- ☐ Current
  - ☐ Historical Document
- ☐ Peer-reviewed by:
  - ☐ Critically reviewed by:
  - ☐ Cited by:
- ☐ Contains a bibliography
- ☐ Contains keywords
- ☐ Contains good quotes
- ☐ Connects to my argument
- ☐ Contradicts my argument

Is the research current, and if not, what is the historical context in which it was produced? What is the general history of this document? Who are the original contributer(s) and author(s)? What other forces have shaped it, political, economic, or otherwise?

How does it support your argument? Explain how it supports your argument.

How does it contradict your argument? Paraphrase or use direct quote and explain the contradiction.

Promising entries from the source's bibliography:

Who is the author? What are the author's credentials? What else has the author written? What is their stance on, or interest in, the topic?

Briefly summarize the source here.

Who is the publisher? What is the publisher's editorial policy? Is the publisher an imprint owned by another company, a website run by a government agency, or a private blog? What is the purpose, or mission, of the publisher?

Source Checklist

- ☐ Authored by a scholar:
  - ☐ Authored by an expert:
  - ☐ Authored by an organization:
  - ☐ Unknown author
- ☐ Published
  - ☐ by a university press:
  - ☐ by another press:
  - ☐ Sponsored by an organization:
- ☐ Primary Source
  - ☐ Secondary Source
  - ☐ Tertiary Source
- ☐ Current
  - ☐ Historical Document
- ☐ Peer-reviewed by:
  - ☐ Critically reviewed by:
  - ☐ Cited by:
- ☐ Contains a bibliography
- ☐ Contains keywords
- ☐ Contains good quotes
- ☐ Connects to my argument
- ☐ Contradicts my argument

Is the research current, and if not, what is the historical context in which it was produced? What is the general history of this document? Who are the original contributer(s) and author(s)? What other forces have shaped it, political, economic, or otherwise?

How does it support your argument? Explain how it supports your argument.

How does it contradict your argument? Paraphrase or use direct quote and explain the contradiction.

Promising entries from the source's bibliography:

Who is the author? What are the author's credentials? What else has the author written? What is their stance on, or interest in, the topic?

Briefly summarize the source here.

Who is the publisher? What is the publisher's editorial policy? Is the publisher an imprint owned by another company, a website run by a government agency, or a private blog? What is the purpose, or mission, of the publisher?

Source Checklist

- ☐ Authored by a scholar:
  - ☐ Authored by an expert:
  - ☐ Authored by an organization:
  - ☐ Unknown author
- ☐ Published
  - ☐ by a university press:
  - ☐ by another press:
  - ☐ Sponsored by an organization:
- ☐ Primary Source
  - ☐ Secondary Source
  - ☐ Tertiary Source
- ☐ Current
  - ☐ Historical Document
- ☐ Peer-reviewed by:
  - ☐ Critically reviewed by:
  - ☐ Cited by:
- ☐ Contains a bibliography
- ☐ Contains keywords
- ☐ Contains good quotes
- ☐ Connects to my argument
- ☐ Contradicts my argument

Is the research current, and if not, what is the historical context in which it was produced? What is the general history of this document? Who are the original contributer(s) and author(s)? What other forces have shaped it, political, economic, or otherwise?

How does it support your argument? Explain how it supports your argument.

How does it contradict your argument? Paraphrase or use direct quote and explain the contradiction.

Promising entries from the source's bibliography:

Who is the author? What are the author's credentials? What else has the author written? What is their stance on, or interest in, the topic?

Briefly summarize the source here.

Who is the publisher? What is the publisher's editorial policy? Is the publisher an imprint owned by another company, a website run by a government agency, or a private blog? What is the purpose, or mission, of the publisher?

Source Checklist

- ☐ Authored by a scholar:
  - ☐ Authored by an expert:
  - ☐ Authored by an organization:
  - ☐ Unknown author
- ☐ Published
  - ☐ by a university press:
  - ☐ by another press:
  - ☐ Sponsored by an organization:
- ☐ Primary Source
  - ☐ Secondary Source
  - ☐ Tertiary Source
- ☐ Current
  - ☐ Historical Document
- ☐ Peer-reviewed by:
  - ☐ Critically reviewed by:
  - ☐ Cited by:
- ☐ Contains a bibliography
- ☐ Contains keywords
- ☐ Contains good quotes
- ☐ Connects to my argument
- ☐ Contradicts my argument

Is the research current, and if not, what is the historical context in which it was produced? What is the general history of this document? Who are the original contributer(s) and author(s)? What other forces have shaped it, political, economic, or otherwise?

How does it support your argument? Explain how it supports your argument.

How does it contradict your argument? Paraphrase or use direct quote and explain the contradiction.

Promising entries from the source's bibliography:

Who is the author? What are the author's credentials? What else has the author written? What is their stance on, or interest in, the topic?

Briefly summarize the source here.

Who is the publisher? What is the publisher's editorial policy? Is the publisher an imprint owned by another company, a website run by a government agency, or a private blog? What is the purpose, or mission, of the publisher?

SOURCE CHECKLIST

- ☐ Authored by a scholar:
  - ☐ Authored by an expert:
  - ☐ Authored by an organization:
  - ☐ Unknown author
- ☐ Published
  - ☐ by a university press:
  - ☐ by another press:
  - ☐ Sponsored by an organization:
- ☐ Primary Source
  - ☐ Secondary Source
  - ☐ Tertiary Source
- ☐ Current
  - ☐ Historical Document
- ☐ Peer-reviewed by:
  - ☐ Critically reviewed by:
  - ☐ Cited by:
- ☐ Contains a bibliography
- ☐ Contains keywords
- ☐ Contains good quotes
- ☐ Connects to my argument
- ☐ Contradicts my argument

Who is the author? What are the author's credentials? What else has the author written? What is their stance on, or interest in, the topic?

Who is the publisher? What is the publisher's editorial policy? Is the publisher an imprint owned by another company, a website run by a government agency, or a private blog? What is the purpose, or mission, of the publisher?

Is the research current, and if not, what is the historical context in which it was produced? What is the general history of this document? Who are the original contributer(s) and author(s)? What other forces have shaped it, political, economic, or otherwise?

How does it support your argument? Explain how it supports your argument.

How does it contradict your argument? Paraphrase or use direct quote and explain the contradiction.

Promising entries from the source's bibliography:

Briefly summarize the source here.

Source Checklist

- ☐ Authored by a scholar:
  - ☐ Authored by an expert:
  - ☐ Authored by an organization:
  - ☐ Unknown author
- ☐ Published
  - ☐ by a university press:
  - ☐ by another press:
  - ☐ Sponsored by an organization:
- ☐ Primary Source
  - ☐ Secondary Source
  - ☐ Tertiary Source
- ☐ Current
  - ☐ Historical Document
- ☐ Peer-reviewed by:
  - ☐ Critically reviewed by:
  - ☐ Cited by:
- ☐ Contains a bibliography
- ☐ Contains keywords
- ☐ Contains good quotes
- ☐ Connects to my argument
- ☐ Contradicts my argument

Is the research current, and if not, what is the historical context in which it was produced? What is the general history of this document? Who are the original contributer(s) and author(s)? What other forces have shaped it, political, economic, or otherwise?

How does it support your argument? Explain how it supports your argument.

How does it contradict your argument? Paraphrase or use direct quote and explain the contradiction.

Promising entries from the source's bibliography:

Who is the author? What are the author's credentials? What else has the author written? What is their stance on, or interest in, the topic?

Briefly summarize the source here.

Who is the publisher? What is the publisher's editorial policy? Is the publisher an imprint owned by another company, a website run by a government agency, or a private blog? What is the purpose, or mission, of the publisher?

SOURCE CHECKLIST

- ☐ Authored by a scholar:
  - ☐ Authored by an expert:
  - ☐ Authored by an organization:
  - ☐ Unknown author
- ☐ Published
  - ☐ by a university press:
  - ☐ by another press:
  - ☐ Sponsored by an organization:
- ☐ Primary Source
  - ☐ Secondary Source
  - ☐ Tertiary Source
- ☐ Current
  - ☐ Historical Document
- ☐ Peer-reviewed by:
  - ☐ Critically reviewed by:
  - ☐ Cited by:
- ☐ Contains a bibliography
- ☐ Contains keywords
- ☐ Contains good quotes
- ☐ Connects to my argument
- ☐ Contradicts my argument

Is the research current, and if not, what is the historical context in which it was produced? What is the general history of this document? Who are the original contributer(s) and author(s)? What other forces have shaped it, political, economic, or otherwise?

How does it support your argument? Explain how it supports your argument.

How does it contradict your argument? Paraphrase or use direct quote and explain the contradiction.

Promising entries from the source's bibliography:

Who is the author? What are the author's credentials? What else has the author written? What is their stance on, or interest in, the topic?

Briefly summarize the source here.

Who is the publisher? What is the publisher's editorial policy? Is the publisher an imprint owned by another company, a website run by a government agency, or a private blog? What is the purpose, or mission, of the publisher?

Source Checklist

- ☐ Authored by a scholar:
  - ☐ Authored by an expert:
  - ☐ Authored by an organization:
  - ☐ Unknown author
- ☐ Published
  - ☐ by a university press:
  - ☐ by another press:
  - ☐ Sponsored by an organization:
- ☐ Primary Source
  - ☐ Secondary Source
  - ☐ Tertiary Source
- ☐ Current
  - ☐ Historical Document
- ☐ Peer-reviewed by:
  - ☐ Critically reviewed by:
  - ☐ Cited by:
- ☐ Contains a bibliography
- ☐ Contains keywords
- ☐ Contains good quotes
- ☐ Connects to my argument
- ☐ Contradicts my argument

Is the research current, and if not, what is the historical context in which it was produced? What is the general history of this document? Who are the original contributer(s) and author(s)? What other forces have shaped it, political, economic, or otherwise?

How does it support your argument? Explain how it supports your argument.

How does it contradict your argument? Paraphrase or use direct quote and explain the contradiction.

Promising entries from the source's bibliography:

Who is the author? What are the author's credentials? What else has the author written? What is their stance on, or interest in, the topic?

Briefly summarize the source here.

Who is the publisher? What is the publisher's editorial policy? Is the publisher an imprint owned by another company, a website run by a government agency, or a private blog? What is the purpose, or mission, of the publisher?

Intro Sketch

List your most relevant sources. Write the last name (or title/publication if author is unknown) for each source. Then briefly summarize the key points of that source.

Here, point out any flaws with your most relevant sources, then note any gaps between these same sources.

Intro Sketch

Based on this research, your own thinking and observations, what is your hypothesis, or proposal?

Why is your proposal important? Who or what does it affect? How does it affect them?

Body Outline

Here you will sketch a loose outline of your content. Summarize all of your assertions, and whatever support you have for that assertion. Acknowledge gaps in your argument, and respond to the arguments of others. Also consider whether your assumptions about the subject area will be contentious or unexpected to your reader.

ASSERTION
SUPPORT
   CONTENTIOUS?
   UNEXPECTED?

ASSERTION
SUPPORT
   CONTENTIOUS?
   UNEXPECTED?

ASSERTION
SUPPORT
   CONTENTIOUS?
   UNEXPECTED?

ASSERTION
SUPPORT
   CONTENTIOUS?
   UNEXPECTED?

ASSERTION
SUPPORT
   CONTENTIOUS?
   UNEXPECTED?

ASSERTION
SUPPORT
   CONTENTIOUS?
   UNEXPECTED?

Body Outline

Imagine the progression, or organization, of your final draft. Is your argument best organized chronologically, topically, or by association? **Using the circles provided**, reorder the sections by writing an order number in the circles provided. When you write the first draft you will use this new order, and each item should be at least one paragraph.

ASSERTION
SUPPORT
   CONTENTIOUS?
   UNEXPECTED?

ASSERTION
SUPPORT
   CONTENTIOUS?
   UNEXPECTED?

ASSERTION
SUPPORT
   CONTENTIOUS?
   UNEXPECTED?

ASSERTION
SUPPORT
   CONTENTIOUS?
   UNEXPECTED?

ASSERTION
SUPPORT
   CONTENTIOUS?
   UNEXPECTED?

ASSERTION
SUPPORT
   CONTENTIOUS?
   UNEXPECTED?

Intro Rewrite

Here you will rework your introduction by adding an opening. Consider a "hook" that helps develop context and draw interest, and empathize with your reader's position. Connect this hook to the greater signficance of your argument. Finish by offering a proposition.

Opening.

Proposal.

Context.

Your research.

Conclusion and Title

Here you can write a conclusion that brings some kind of closure to your argument, while at the same time offering additional significance, or importance, and making a specific call for additional research beyond what you've written in this essay, making plain the potential opportunities for future inquiry (not addressed by this essay). Start with a general closing that echoes, but does not copy, your introduction.

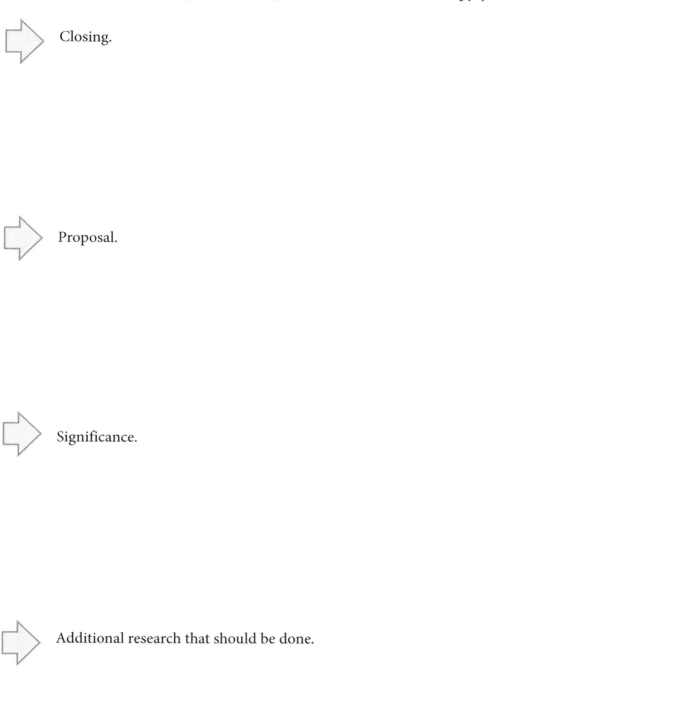

Closing.

Proposal.

Significance.

Additional research that should be done.

Conclusion and Title

WHAT'S YOUR TITLE?
Your title should be specific to your proposal.

Jane Doe

Professor Pfannkuchen

English 110-01

September 1, 2019

Centered Title

Begin by setting up your document. Go to Document Settings, and then to Margins. The margins of your essay should be 1" (one inch) all around (top, bottom, left, and right). Make sure your font is Times New Roman, 12 point font. Your entire essay should be "double spaced".

Above, starting with "Doe 1" in the upper right hand corner, is the "running header". You need to access the "header" in whatever application you're using, write your last name, and then to to [Insert > Page Number]. The "insert page number" option in most applications automatically numbers your pages for you. It's "right aligned" which means that it will always stick to the right side of the header.

The next thing you'll see are on the left hand side, starting with "Jane Doe" on the first line, and then ending with "September 1, 2019" on the last line. That is a standard MLA (Modern Language Association) heading. The first line is always the name of the student or essayist. The second line is the professor's name, usually with "Professsor," or "Prof." before their actual name. The third line is the course name or course title. And the fourth line is the date. You'll want to use the date that you finished the essay. The heading is "left aligned," without any indents or extra spacing.

The next line you see at the top is the Centered Title. This is where the title of your essay goes. The title is capitalized, according to MLA style, which means important or meaningful words are capitalized, while unimportant words like "a" or "the" usually aren't (unless they are the first word in the title). The centered title is "center aligned" which means it will always be at the center of the page.

Your essay, indented .5". Press the tab button on your keyboard at the beginning of each new paragraph, unless of course the application you're using has already indented the paragraph half an inch already.

Below it says to insert a page break. That's something relatively universal in writing applications. What it means is go to the insert menu at the top of the application and choose the page break option. That will push the Works Cited page onto the next page. This is much better than trying to hit the enter button enough times to get the works cited page to the top of the next page, since a page break will do that for you automatically, regardless of any changes you may make to the essay.

The works cited entries are in hanging indent format. It's litereally the opposite of a half inch indent. In hanging indent the first line of the paragraph comes all the way to the left margin, while the rest of the paragraph is indented half an inch. This way the first line sticks out more than the rest of the paragraph. This is so people can easily scan the left margin of your works cited and find the author they are looking for.

[Insert > Page Break]

Works Cited

Works Cited Last, First. Title of Source. Title of Container. Title of Publisher. Publication Date.

Location.

Works Cited Last, First. Title of Source. Title of Container. Title of Publisher. Publication Date.

Location.

Works Cited Last, First. Title of Source. Title of Container. Title of Publisher. Publication Date.

Location.

Made in the USA
Middletown, DE
31 January 2019